An ECS **Once Upon A Time**™ Book, Grades K-2

Jack and the Beanstalk

Critical Thinking and Writing Activities
For the Emerging Reader

Arlene Capriola and Rigmor Swensen
Illustrated by Kathy Burns

Welcome to the Once Upon A Time™ series!

Learning to read should be fun! Children focus longer and retain more when they are doing activities they enjoy. The 10-book **Once Upon A Time**™ series teaches reading and writing as a fun, engaging process. Children create their own storybooks (complete with illustrations!) by elaborating on well-known fairy tales. Familiar story lines and colorful characters will amuse and entertain children for hours as they improve reading and writing skills.

The **Once Upon A Time**™ series is more than just fun. It is an effective means of advancing reading and writing levels. Educators agree that emerging readers should begin reading with materials that provide higher-level thinking skills and practice in following directions. Research emphasizes that reading and writing should begin simultaneously. The **Once Upon A Time**™ series provides these elements in a format attractive to children. Each book in the series encourages:

- Reading beyond the blank before answering, learning to use context clues
- Rereading each completed chapter, asking, "Does your story make sense?"
- Referring to the story for clues to answer TELL and GUESS questions
- Becoming involved in the story and risk-taking
- Reading directions carefully prior to drawing comprehension pictures
- Using complete sentences for all writing activities

Welcome to the fairy-tale world of learning with the **Once Upon A Time**™ series! Have fun!

About the Authors...

Arlene Capriola, an elementary reading specialist, holds a combined master's degree in reading and learning disabilities. She has three sons and resides with her husband, John, in Long Island, New York.

Rigmor Swensen is a freelance writer and former teacher of secondary reading and English literature. She holds a master's degree in reading and special education. Riggie, mother of three, lives in Long Island, New York, with her husband, Roy. She and Arlene have enjoyed collaborating on several reading workbook series.

 The Once Upon A Time™ series is also available on audio tapes!

To order, contact your local school supply store or –
ECS Learning Systems, Inc.
P.O. Box 791437
San Antonio, Texas 78279-1437

Editor: Cherisse Mastry
Cover/Page Layout & Graphics: Kirstin Simpson
Book Design: Educational Media Services

ISBN 1-57022-142-1

©1998 by ECS Learning Systems, Inc., San Antonio, Texas. All rights reserved. No part of this publication may be reproduced, stored in a retrieval system, or transmitted in any way or by any means (electronic, mechanical, photocopying, recording, or otherwise) without prior written permission from ECS Learning Systems, Inc., with the exceptions found below.

Photocopying of student worksheets by a teacher who purchased this publication for his/her own class is permissible. Reproduction of any part of this publication for an entire school or for a school system or for commercial sale is strictly prohibited. **Copyright infringement is a violation of Federal Law.**

Printed in the United States of America.

My Story about...

(Draw your own cover.)

Jack and the Beanstalk

by

_____

(Write your name.)

Chapter 1

Jack and his mother lived on a farm.

They had no food and they had no money.

All they _____ was a fine brown cow.
       (had, did)

One _____ their money was gone.
     (dog, day)

"Take the cow to town," Mother said.

"Sell her _____ the market.
          (at, come)

Be sure to get a lot of money for her."

So Jack went down _____ path.
                   (the, to)

_____ had the cow on a rope.
(He, Him)

Soon he met a funny man.

Guess: What will the man say?

The man will _____

_____

Jack and his mother are on the little farm.
Who else lives with them?

- Go dot-to-dot to show it.

©ECS Learning Systems, Inc., San Antonio, TX   All rights reserved   5

Chapter 2

The man said, "Let me have your cow.

I will _____ you five magic beans.
        (have, give)

They will get you many things."

So Jack gave him the cow for the beans.

Jack _____ happy.
     (was, wish)

He ran home to show Mother the beans.

But Mother was **not** happy.

"**Now** what will we _____?" she asked.
                     (do, stop)

"We have no _____ and no money!"
           (cow, rag)

Then she tossed the beans out the window.

She and Jack went to _____.
                     (saw, bed)

Guess: What will the beans do?

The beans will _____

_____

Make the pictures tell the story.

- Put **1** in the box that comes **first**.
- Put **2** in the box that comes **next**.
- Put **3** in the box that comes **last**.

Chapter 3

In the morning Jack looked out the window.

He had to _____ his eyes.
(bill, rub)

There was a very big beanstalk!

Jack went outside and looked up.

The beanstalk _____ very tall.
(was, can)

It was so tall it hid the sun.

Jack could not _____ the top of it.
(see, stop)

"I will climb up into the sky," he said.

Jack climbed and he _____ .
(climbed, bid)

At last he came to the _____ .
(pit, top)

He saw a big red house far away.

Guess: Who lives in the big red house?

I think _____

_____

Jack is going to the big red house.

- Help him get there.
- Choose the best path.

Chapter 4

"I will go to that house," he said.

"Maybe there will be _____ for me."
(frogs, food)

Jack ran to the house.

A giant woman came to the door.

"Go away!" she called.

"This is the _____ of the giant!
(car, house)

He likes to eat little boys!"

Jack _____ afraid.
(sat, was)

But he said, "Please let me come in.

I must eat and rest a bit."

At last the _____ woman said yes.
(little, giant)

She gave Jack _____ and bread.
(jam, sand)

Guess: Uh, oh! Will the giant come?

_____ , the giant _____
(Yes, No)

_____

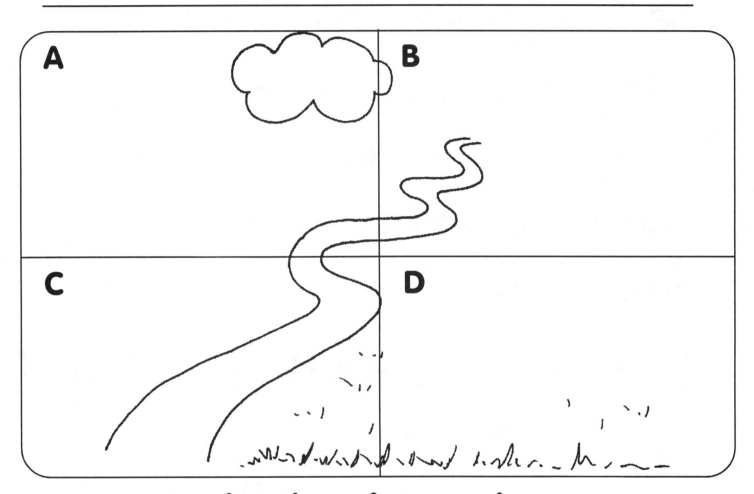

Make the picture show what was in the sky.

- Make a yellow sun in box **A**.
- Make two green trees in box **D**.
- Make a big red house in box **B**.
- Make the top of the beanstalk in box **C**.

Chapter 5

Just then, there was a big **thump, thump**.

"The giant is coming!" said the woman.

"Come, hide _____ the oven!"
(to, in)

Jack jumped into the oven just _____ time.
(up, in)

In came the giant calling,

"**Fee, fi, fo, fum**.

I smell the blood of a little one."

"No one is here," said his _____ .
(baby, wife)

"Come and _____ down."
(sit, bat)

"**Bring me my meal then**," said the giant.

The giant _____ a big cow.
(let, ate)

Then he called, "**Bring me my gold!**"

Guess: What will the giant do now?

The giant will _____

_____

Color the picture of the giant's house:

- The thing Jack hides in is black.
- The thing the giant sits on is brown.
- The one who eats a cow has a red hat.
- The one who lets Jack in has a blue dress.

Chapter 6

His wife gave him six big gold blocks.

The giant liked to _____ at them.
(look, dance)

"Z-z-z-z." Soon he _____ to sleep.
(took, went)

Jack jumped out of the _____ .
(hat, oven)

He went to the table and took the gold.

Out the _____ he ran!
(boat, door)

Jack ran to the beanstalk and slid _____ .
(up, down)

He told Mother all about the giant.

Then he showed her all the gold.

Jack and Mother had food for a long time.

But one day the gold was gone.

Guess: Oh, no! What will Jack do now?

Jack will _____

_____

How did Jack get home?

- Put a ⬭ on the picture that shows it.
- **Color** the thing he slid down green.

Chapter 7

Jack went back up the beanstalk.

He _____ up, up into the sky.
(sent, climbed)

He ran to the giant's big, red _____ .
(stop, house)

This time the giant's wife _____ mad.
(set, was)

"You cannot come in!" she said.

"Last time you took the giant's gold!"

Jack had to beg and beg.

At last the giant woman let _____ in.
(Mother, Jack)

Just then, there was a big **thump, thump**.

"The giant is coming!" said the woman.

"Come, _____ in this pot!"
(same, hide)

Guess: Will the giant find Jack?

I think the giant _____

_____

Here is Jack at the giant's house.

But 4 things are missing.

- **Draw** them.
- **Color** the picture.

Chapter 8

Jack jumped in the big pot _____ in time.
(off, just)

In came the giant calling,

"Fee, fi, fo, fum,

I smell the blood of a little one!"

"There is no one here," said his wife.

"Come here and sit _____ ."
(out, down)

"Bring me my meal, then," the giant said.

He ate a big tub full _____ fish.
(by, of)

Then the giant called, **"Bring me my hen!"**

He said to it, **"Lay a gold egg!"**

Cluck! Cluck! Out came a gold _____ .
(table, egg)

Jack looked out of the _____ .
(cap, pot)

Guess: Will Jack take the hen?

I think _____

_____

Here is the giant with the hen.

- What does he say? **Write** it.
- What does the hen say? **Write** that, too.

Chapter 9

"**Z-z-z-z.**" Soon the giant went to sleep.

Jack jumped out of the pot and got the hen.

He _____ to the beanstalk.
　　　(fell, ran)

He slid all the way down and was home!

The hen laid a gold egg every _____ .
　　　　　　　　　　　　　　　　　　(day, kid)

Jack and Mother had lots of food.

But one day Jack went back up the beanstalk.

He ran up to the giant's red _____ .
　　　　　　　　　　　　　　(lamp, house)

Jack had to beg and _____ to come in.
　　　　　　　　　　　(beg, bill)

Just then, there was a big **thump, thump**.

"The giant is coming!" said the woman.

"Come, hide in _____ pail!"
　　　　　　　　(this, thump)

Guess: What will the giant say?

The giant will say _____

_____

Who am I? Put the letter.

____ I said, "Fee, fi, fo, fum."   ____ I sent Jack to town.
____ I gave Jack the beans.   ____ I let Jack in my home.

Chapter 10

Jack jumped _____ the pail just in time.
(but, into)

In came the _____ calling,
(mouse, giant)

"**Fee, fi, fo, fum,**

I smell the blood of a little one!"

"There is no one here," said his wife.

"Come _____ and sit down."
(put, here)

"**Bring me my meal, then**," the giant said.

The giant _____ 60 birds.
(ate, was)

Then he called, "**Bring me my harp!**"

He _____ to the harp, "**Play a song!**"
(said, had)

The harp did play the best _____!
(table, song)

"**Z-z-z-z**." Soon the giant went to sleep.

Guess: What will Jack do now?

I think Jack will _____

_____

Make the Picture

The giant is sleeping.
Tell Jack what he must do now.

• Put the first letter for each picture.

Chapter 11

Jack jumped out of the pot and got the harp.

But the harp called, "Master! Master!"

The giant was up and after Jack!

He put out his _____ hand to grab Jack.
(big, little)

Jack _____ down the beanstalk.
(slid, put)

But the giant was coming down after him!

Jack got an _____ and chopped.
(apple, ax)

Crash!

Down came the giant with the beanstalk!

And that was the _____ of the giant!
(hat, end)

Now Jack and Mother had all they wanted.

They were very _____ .
(happy, big)

Tell: Can Jack go up the beanstalk again?

Jack _____ go up again because
(can, can't)

_____

Who did this?

1. He says, "Fe, fi, fo, fum."
2. He climbed up the beanstalk.
3. She wanted to sell the cow.
4. Jack gave her to the man.

Instant Recap

Here is the story of Jack and the Beanstalk again.
Write the words to tell the story.
The word box will help you.

Jack and his mother lived on a farm. They were

very poor. One day they had no _____ left.

Jack's mother told him to go to town to sell the cow.

On the path Jack met a little man. He gave the man

his cow for five magic _____ . But Mother was

mad. She tossed the beans out the window.

The next day Jack saw a big, big _____ .

He went up the beanstalk to the _____ . He ran

to the giant's house, and the giant's wife let him in.

When the giant came, _____ said, "**Fee, fi, fo, fum.

I smell the blood of a little one**." Jack hid in the oven.

When the giant went to _____ , Jack jumped

out of the oven and took the giant's gold.

Mother and Jack had lots to eat. But one day the

gold was gone. So _____ went back up the

beanstalk. This time the giant's wife hid him in a big pot.

When the giant went to sleep, Jack jumped out of the

_____ and took the hen. Jack _____

home. Soon he went back to the giant's house. This time

he took the giant's harp. But the giant came after him.

Jack slid down and chopped down the beanstalk. That

was the end of the giant! Now Jack and Mother are

very _____ .

The End

ran	sleep	pot	beanstalk	money
sky	Jack	he	happy	beans

Lost Bag of Gold

Today I lost _____
(Tell what he lost.)

I was sitting _____
(Tell where he was sitting.)

My bag of gold was _____
(Where was it?)

When I woke up _____
(Tell what he saw.)

If you find my bag of gold, please call:

_____
(Write your telephone number.)

The giant did not know where his bag of gold went. He put this note on all the trees and in all the shops. Help him tell all about his missing gold.

McGiant's Restaurant
Menu

For Dinner

60 Big Burgers	300 dollars
Tub of Fries	200 dollars
100 Hot Pizzas	500 dollars

After Dinner

4 Apple Pies	10 dollars
30 Cup Cakes	20 dollars
Giant Ice Cream	60 dollars

The giant and his wife went out for dinner.
Pick what they will eat.

For dinner the giant will eat _____ .

After dinner he will have _____ .

His wife will eat _____ .

After dinner she will have _____ .

Author's Page

You are the author.
Draw your picture in the box below.

1. **Read** your story to five others.

2. **Tell** them to put their names below.

3. Let them **tell** you how they like your story.

4. Let them **tell** you how they like your pictures.

(Write your name.)

NO LONGER THE PROPERTY
OF THE
UNIVERSITY OF R.I. LIBRARY